ISBN 1-85576-010-X
Illustrations copyright © 1990 Gerald Hawksley
Text copyright © 1990 Treehouse Children's Books Ltd
Published by Treehouse Children's Books Ltd 1990
All rights reserved
Printed in Spain by Salingraf, S. A. L.

MAGGIE'S FARM

Words by Caroline Cary
Pictures by Gerald Hawksley

TREEHOUSE

"Cock-a-doodle-doo!" crows the cockerel.
It is early morning on Maggie's farm.
The wheat is ripe, it's harvest time.
But first Maggie must milk the cows.

Here are Tom, John, Bob, Ben and George.
They all work on the farm too.
CHUG-A-CHUG-A-CHUG . . . John starts the tractor.
Tom starts the combine harvester, ready for work.

milking-machine

"Moo, moo," low the cows in the milking-parlour.
"Baa, baa," says a sheep.
"What are you doing here?" asks Maggie. She puts
the milking-machine on. SHHH-UP . . . SHHH-UP . . .

pick-up truck

After milking, the cows go back to the fields.
''I'll take you home,'' says Maggie to the sheep,
and puts him in her pick-up truck. Maggie uses her
pick-up truck for driving over rough ground.

sledge-hammer

But when Maggie reaches the sheep pasture, all the sheep are gone. A fence post has fallen over and the wire has broken. Maggie knocks the post back into the ground with her sledge-hammer.

wire-cutters

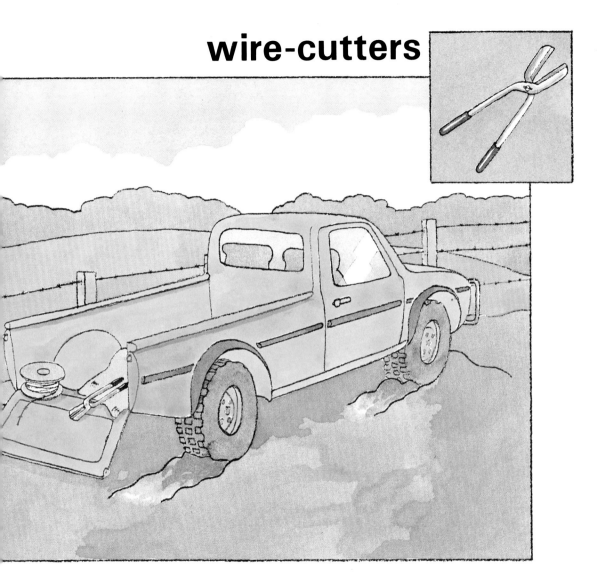

Then she takes out her wire-cutters and some wire, and stretches a new piece across the gap.
"That will keep you in," says Maggie. "Now I'll go and find your friends."

combine harvester

Tom is driving the combine harvester.
PAH-DUM . . . PAH-DUM . . . the big blades turn

and cut the tall wheat. It strips the grain
from the stalks. The stalks are left for straw.

trailer

The wheat grain is poured into the trailer towed
by John's tractor. When his trailer is full,
he takes the grain away to be dried and stored.
''Enough to make bread for a year,'' laughs Tom.

tractor

John's tractor is very powerful. It has big wheels so it can drive over bumpy and slippery fields. The tractor powers most of the machines on the farm as it tows them along.

Here are some more machines powered by tractors:

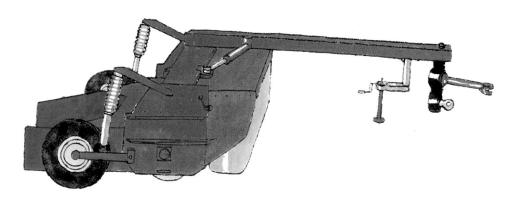

The **mowing-machine** cuts the long green grass.

The **rake** gathers the cut grass into rows to dry.
Dried grass is called hay. It is kept to feed
the cows in winter.

The **forage-harvester** cuts the grass, chops it up and pumps it into a trailer. The grass is pressed and made into silage, which is also used to feed the cows in the winter.

baler

Bob is towing a baler behind his tractor.
It gathers the straw into bundles called bales.
''Have you seen my sheep?'' asks Maggie.
Bob shakes his head.

plough

Ben's tractor is pulling a plough. The plough
digs the ground, burying the old wheat stubble.
''Have you seen my sheep?'' asks Maggie.
Ben shakes his head.

harrow

The harrow pulled by George's tractor breaks up
the ploughed ground ready for seed to be planted.
''Have you seen my sheep?'' asks Maggie.
George shakes his head.

seed-drill

The new seed is planted by a seed-drill pulled
by Tom's tractor. Maggie stops Tom.
''Have you seen my sheep?'' she asks.
Tom shakes his head.

muck-spreader

John's tractor is pulling a muck-spreader.
It spills manure on the ground to make the grass
grow better. ''Pooh!'' says Maggie. ''Have you seen
my sheep?'' John shakes his head.

Maggie drives home for lunch. ''Salad today,
I think,'' says Maggie. But what does she see?
Her sheep in her garden, eating her vegetables.
''Oh no!'' says Maggie. ''What am I going to eat?''

Maggie drives the sheep back to their field. She stops on the way to buy bread, butter and cheese. ''I wonder,'' says Maggie, ''if it was made from the wheat and milk from my farm?''